THOMAS F. DUNHILL

FIRST YEAR PIECES

FELIX SWINSTEAD

WORK AND PLAY

THE ASSOCIATED BOARD OF
THE ROYAL SCHOOLS OF MUSIC

Thomas Frederick Dunhill, the English composer and teacher, was born in London in 1877 and died at Scunthorpe in 1946. He entered the Royal College of Music in 1893, where he studied composition under Sir Charles Stanford. He subsequently taught at Eton College and at the R.C.M. He first made his name as a composer of chamber music, and later he turned his attention more to the orchestra. He wrote the music for two ballets and also composed some light operas, including the successful *Tantivy Towers*. His educational output, particularly for the piano, was quite extensive. His studies and pieces are never lacking in musical interest, and they still prove to be popular and useful among teachers today.

FIRST YEAR PIECES

1
Melody in C

THOMAS F. DUNHILL

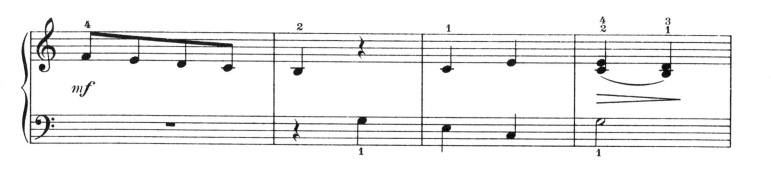

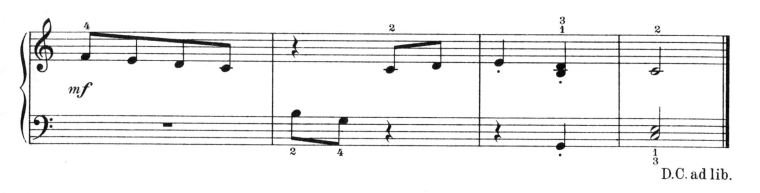

D.C. ad lib.

AB 1944

2
The Sheep on the Downs

D.C. ad lib.

AB 1944

3
The Old Windmill

4
The Old Abbey

5
A little Hush-Song

6
Where the nodding Violet grows

7
On the River Bank

8
A Song of Erin

9
Gavotte in G

10
A Sad Story

11
Swaying Branches

12
Jock plays the Bagpipes

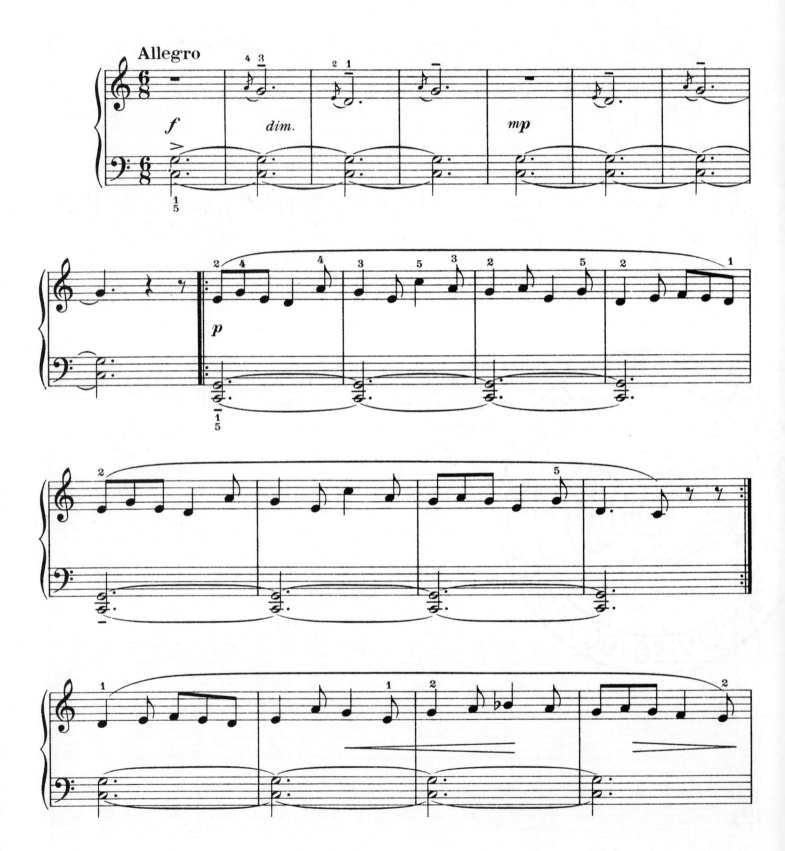

Felix Swinstead, the English composer, pianist and teacher, was born in London in 1880 and died in 1959. He studied at the Royal Academy of Music from 1897 to 1901 and ten years later was appointed pianoforte professor there. For many years he was an examiner of the Associated Board. His published works were numerous, mainly consisting of pieces for the piano, often written for educational purposes. His simpler pieces, like the album *Work and Play*, are full of character and are more than mere pedagogic exercises; they still remain popular with teachers after fifty years.

WORK AND PLAY

1
An Old Garden

FELIX SWINSTEAD

AB 1944

2
Night March

FELIX SWINSTEAD

3
Resting

FELIX SWINSTEAD

4
Up with the Lark

FELIX SWINSTEAD

5
Polly put the Kettle on

FELIX SWINSTEAD

6
The Lonely Road

FELIX SWINSTEAD

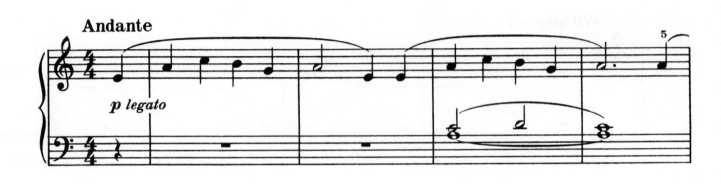

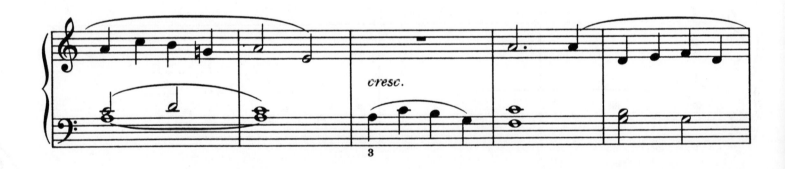

7
Follow my Leader

FELIX SWINSTEAD

8
Eastern Dance

FELIX SWINSTEAD

9
On the Lake

FELIX SWINSTEAD

10
Gavotte

FELIX SWINSTEAD

Steady, well marked time

11
Sailor's Song

FELIX SWINSTEAD

12
Gliding

FELIX SWINSTEAD

Reproduced and printed by
Halstan & Co. Ltd., Amersham, Bucks., England   AB 1944   5/90